In this comic

Superman

Batman

Chip

Super-Dog

Princess

The Flash

Jumpa

Ace

Green Lantern

Aquaman

Streaky

Topo

Beppo

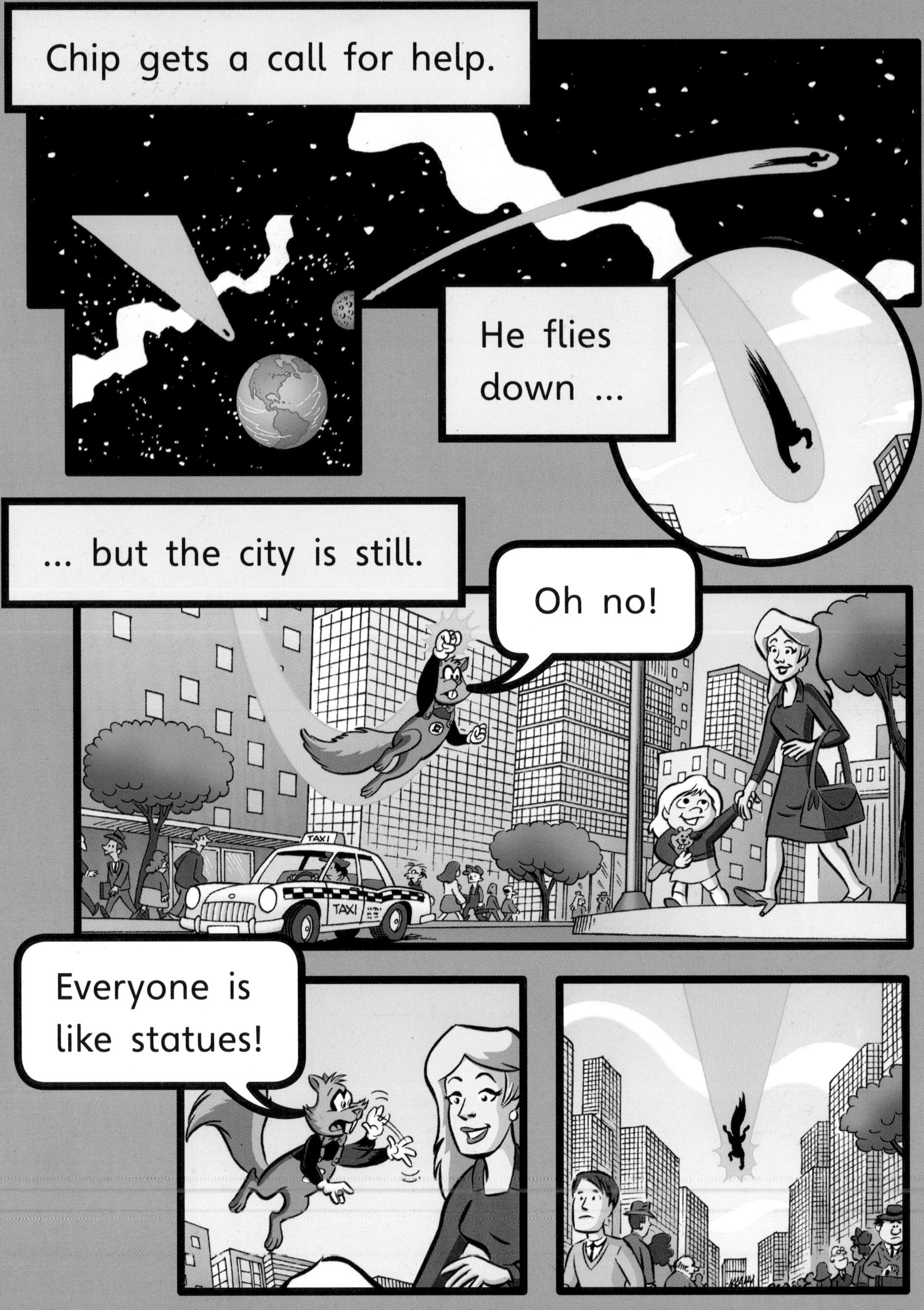
Chip gets a call for help.
He flies down ...
... but the city is still.
Oh no!
TAXI
TAXI
Everyone is like statues!

Help us!
Why are you like statues?
The Super Friends are stuck too!
It started at the Peace Council ....
Out of my way!
Oce!
I am Kanjar! I will rule you all!
Boo!
Hiss!
ARGENTINA
ARMENIA
Nonsense! Call the Super Friends!

Here we come!
My fancy gong will turn everyone into statues ....
Bong!
Bong!
Bong!
Oh no!
We are stuck! But the pets are still free.
So you called me!
Yes! Find all the Super-Pets!

The Super-Pets fly in ...
Force Kanjar to cancel this curse!
We will!
We promise.

What a scene! You are just a council of fancy statues!
The Super-Pets are here!
Oh no!

Ha ha ha ha ha!
We have the gong stick. You are beaten!
Nice one, Super-Dog!
Look! A crack!
The roof is falling!

We can fix it!
Nice job!
Stop Kanjar!

One bounce ...
Boing!

... and a tail flick ....
... should get him!
Yikes!
Crash!

Now set everyone free!
I have no choice.
EXIT
This will do it but we must go outside.
Blow it, Kanjar!
Fweeeet!

But they are still statues!
Fools! The whistling was a trick!
I have called my Ant Force!
Skit Skut
Skit Skut
Skit Skut

There are too many!
Princess shouts for help.
Beppo! Go to the space base.

There it is!
Listen to my voice! Press the sphere.
It turns you into a man ....
.... and turns us ....
.... into apes!

We are free again!
Super-Apes go!
We can take on the ants.
Put them in a spin.
Whizz
Whizz

Blow them away!
Clean them up!
Skudder
Skudder
Skudder
You have no defence!
B-b-but ...
Where will I go?
To a prison cell!

Back at the space base ...
To cancel the curse ....
... press twice!
Yippee!
We did it!
Hooray!
Great job, Super-Pets!